GREAT PIANO SOLOS

THE BLACK BOOK

THE BLUE BOOK
Titles include
Rhapsody In Blue, Moon River, Take Five,
Don't Cry For Me Argentina, theme from "The Piano"
and forty-two more classic pieces.
AM952215

THE RED BOOK
Titles include
Nessun Dorma, Smoke Gets In Your Eyes, The Girl From Ipanema,
The Music Of The Night, Love Theme from "Romeo And Juliet"
and forty-three more classic pieces.
AM952226

THE WHITE BOOK
Titles include
Bali Ha'i (From "South Pacific"), Bridge Over Troubled Water,
Live And Let Die, Come Fly With Me, Jupiter (From "The Planets")
and thirty-five more classic pieces.
AM89692

THE PLATINUM BOOK
Titles include
Pachelbel's Canon, After Midnight (From "Chicago"),
Crazy, Don't Know Why, You'll Never Walk Alone
and thirty-six more classic pieces.
AM89684

FOR MORE BOOKS IN THE GREAT PIANO SOLOS SERIES
GO TO WWW.MUSICROOM.COM

GREAT PIANO SOLOS

Wise Publications
London/New York/Paris/Sydney/Copenhagen/Berlin/Madrid/Tokyo

Published by
Wise Publications
14-15 Berners Street, London W1T 3LJ, UK

Exclusive Distributors:
Music Sales Limited
Distribution Centre, Newmarket Road,
Bury St Edmunds, Suffolk IP33 3YB, UK.

Music Sales Pty Limited
20 Resolution Drive, Caringbah,
NSW 2229, Australia.

Order No. AM970167R
ISBN: 1-84609-389-9
This book © Copyright 2002 Wise Publications,
a division of Music Sales Limited.

Your Guarantee of Quality:
As publishers, we strive to produce every book to the highest commercial
standards. This book has been carefully designed to minimise awkward
page turns and to make playing from it a real pleasure. Particular care has
been given to specifying acid-free, neutral-sized paper made from pulps
which have not been elemental chlorine bleached. This pulp is from farmed
sustainable forests and was produced with special regard for the
environment. Throughout, the printing and binding have been planned to
ensure a sturdy, attractive publication which should give years of
enjoyment. If your copy fails to meet our high standards, please inform us
and we will gladly replace it.

www.musicsales.com

CONTENTS

Adagio For Strings, Op.11

By Samuel Barber

Molto adagio (very slowly)

(with increasing intensity)

mf espr.

f

cresc. sempre

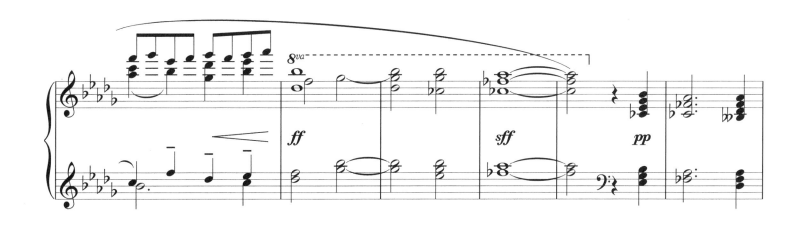

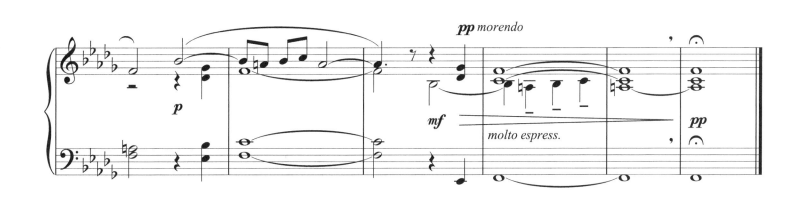

Air On The G String
(from "Suite No. 3 in D")

By Johann Sebastian Bach

Clair de Lune
(from "Suite Bergamasque")

By Claude Debussy

Andante très expressif

peu à peu cresc. et animé

un poco mosso

8va-------------

dim. molto

pp

En animant

Tempo I

pp morendo jusqu'à la fin

Für Elise

By Ludwig Van Beethoven

meno mosso

rit.

Morning
(from "Peer Gynt")

By Edvard Grieg

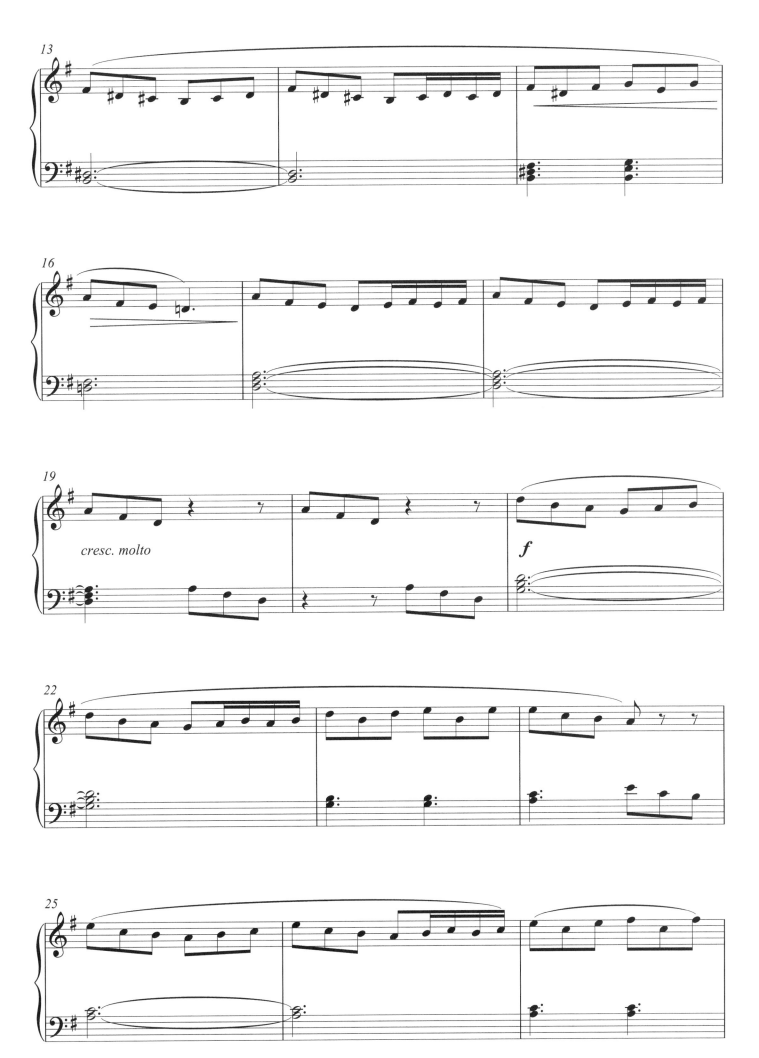

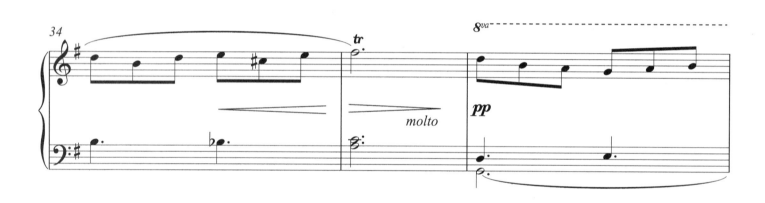

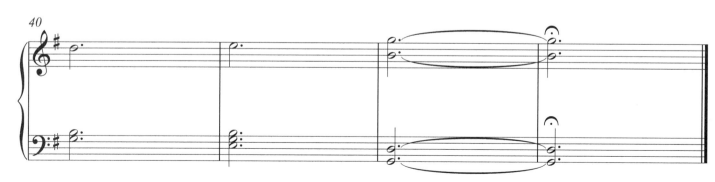

Prelude in E Minor, Op.28 No.4

By Frederic Chopin

Pie Jesu

(from "Requiem, Op.48")

By Gabriel Fauré

Rondo Alla Turca
(from "Piano Sonata No.11 in A Major")

By Wolfgang Amadeus Mozart

American Beauty / Angela Undress
(from "American Beauty")

By Thomas Newman

I. MAIN THEME

II. ANGELA UNDRESS

Cavatina
(from "The Deer Hunter")

By Stanley Myers

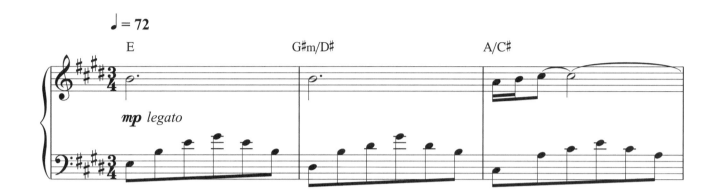

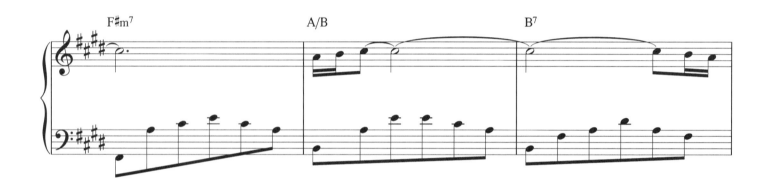

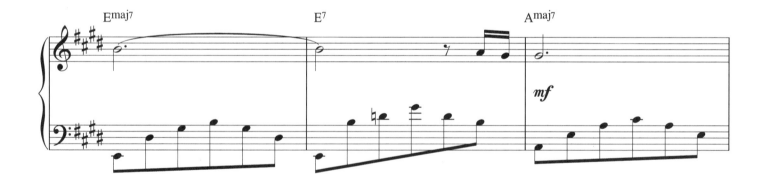

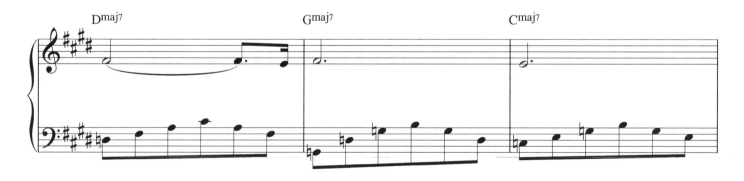

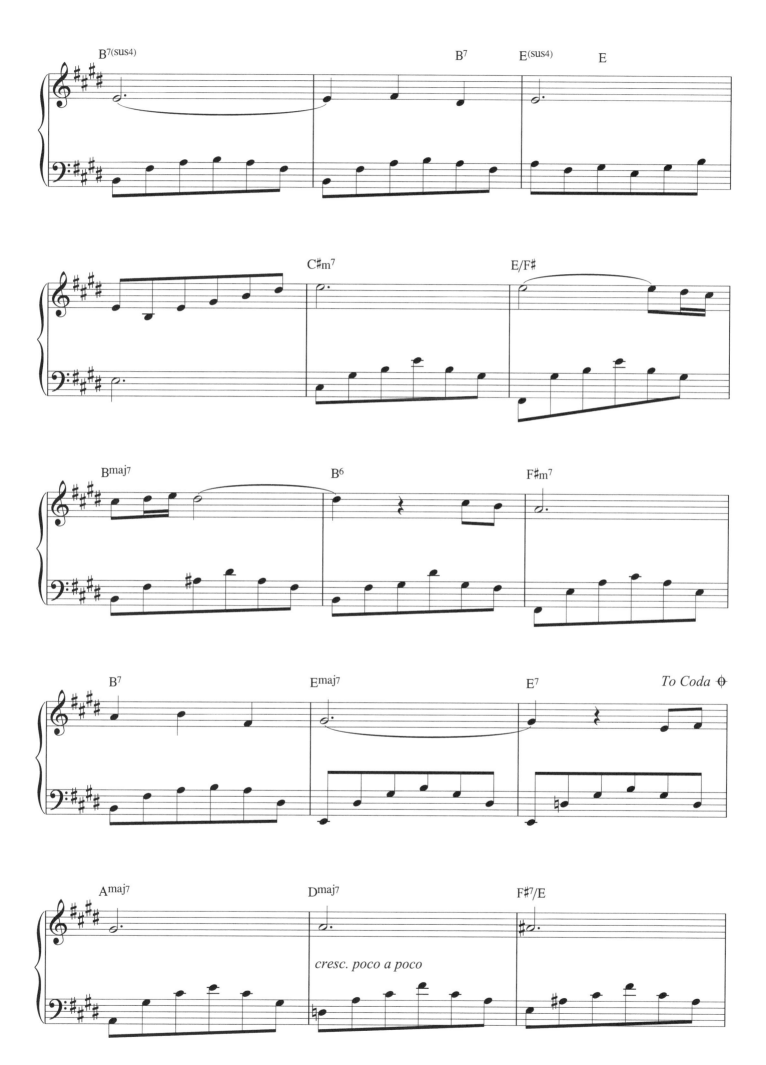

Crouching Tiger, Hidden Dragon / Eternal Vow
(from "Crouching Tiger, Hidden Dragon")

By Tan Dun

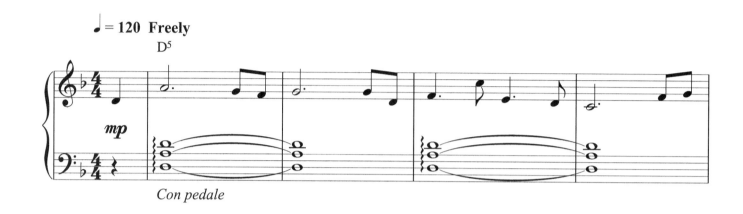

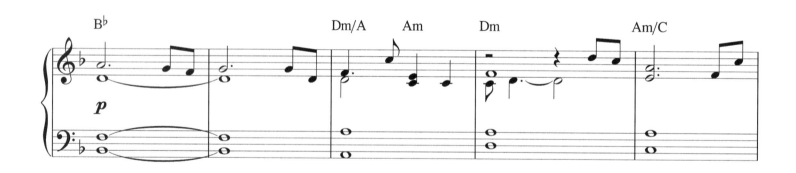

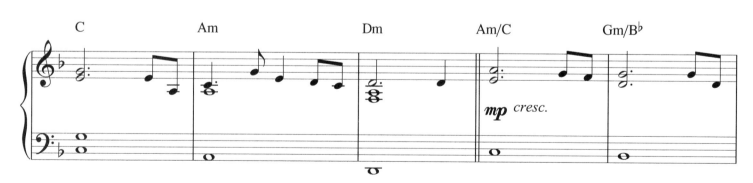

Feather Theme
(Main Title from the film "Forrest Gump")

By Alan Silvestri

43

(lightly)

44

For The Love Of A Princess

(from "Braveheart")

By James Horner

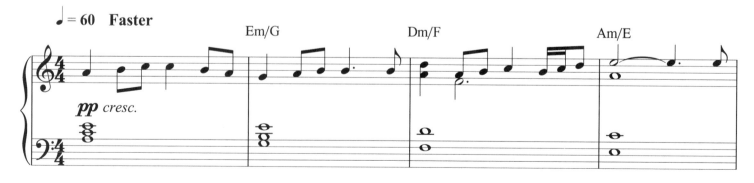

Lara's Theme
(from "Doctor Zhivago")

By Maurice Jarre

Raiders March
(from "Raiders Of The Lost Ark")

By John Williams

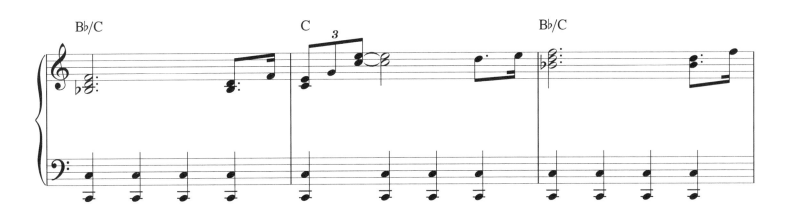

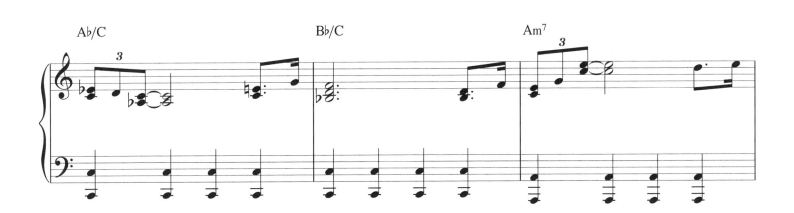

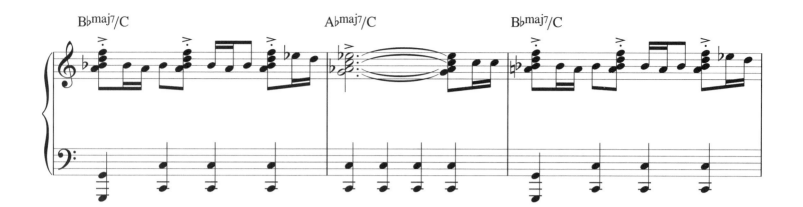

The Beginning Of The Partnership

(from "Shakespeare In Love")

By Stephen Warbeck

All I Have To Do Is Dream

Words & Music by Boudleaux Bryant

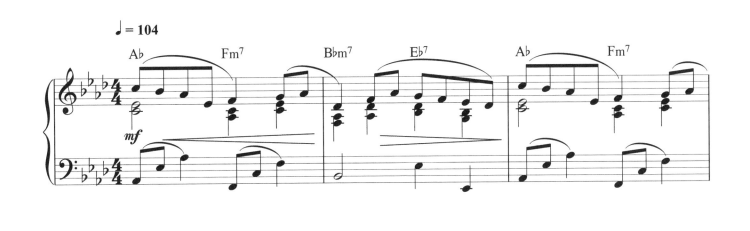

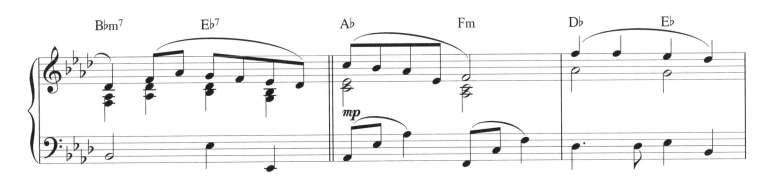

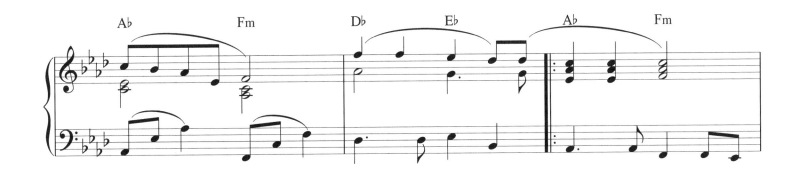

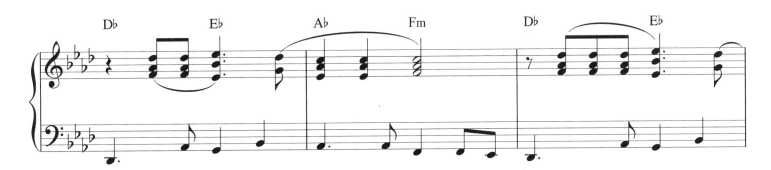

My Way

Words & Music by Claude Francois, Jacques Revaux & Gilles Thibaut

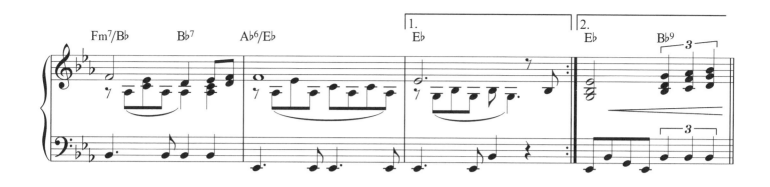

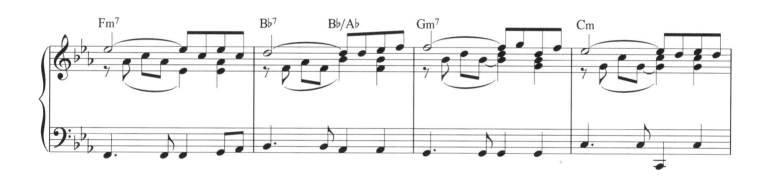

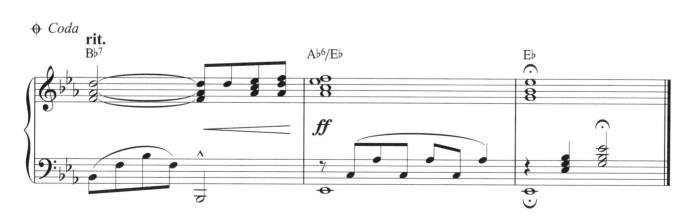

Can't Help Falling In Love

Words & Music by George David Weiss, Hugo Peretti & Luigi Creatore

Somethin' Stupid

Words & Music by C. Carson Parks

Stardust

Words by Mitchell Parish
Music by Hoagy Carmichael

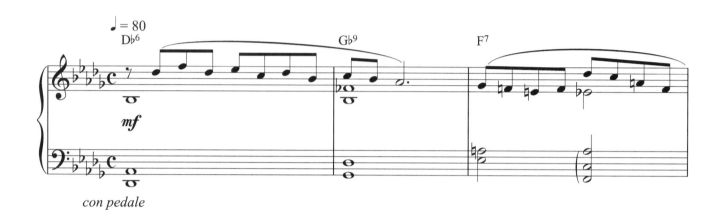

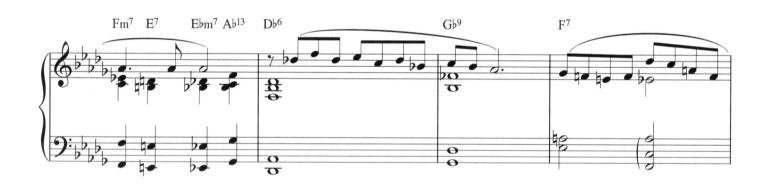

When I Fall In Love

Music by Victor Young
Words by Edward Heyman

What The World Needs Now Is Love

Words by Hal David
Music by Burt Bacharach

Unchained Melody

Words by Hy Zaret
Music by Alex North

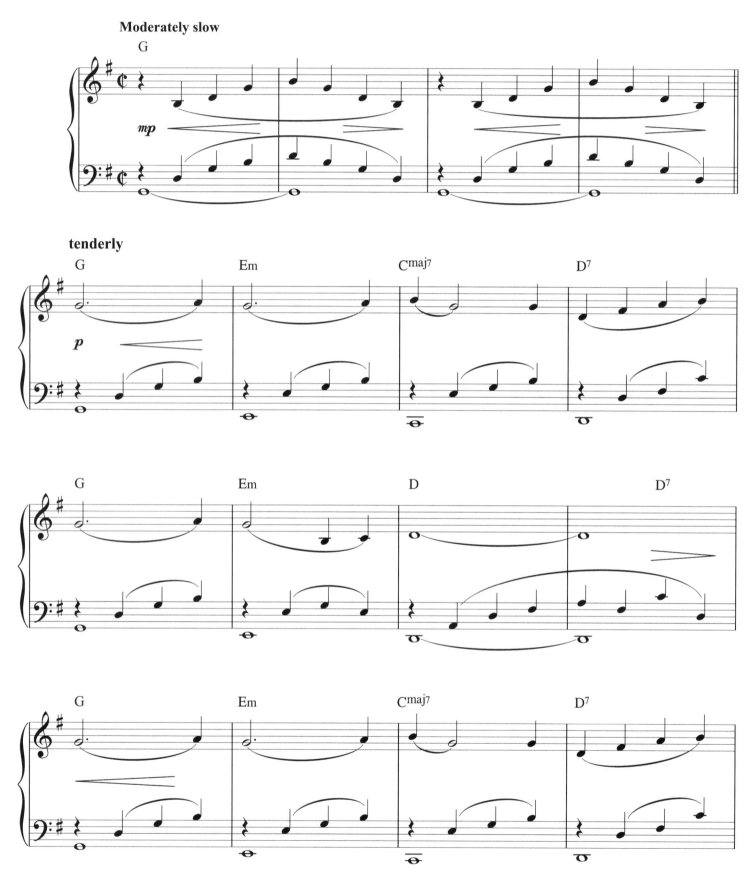

tempo primo

Ain't Misbehavin'

Words by Andy Razaf
Music by Thomas 'Fats' Waller & Harry Brooks

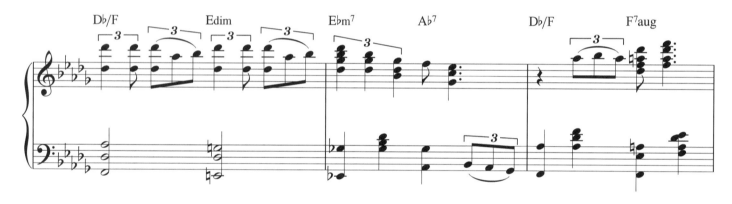

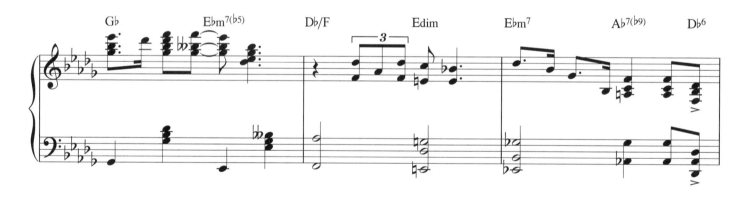

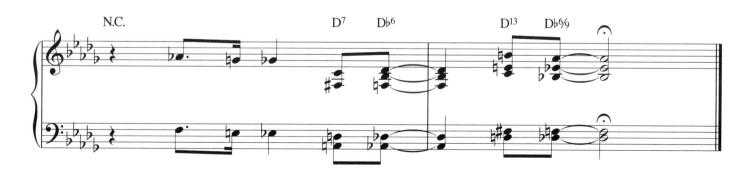

The Entertainer

By Scott Joplin

I Wish I Knew How It Would Feel To Be Free

Words by Billy Taylor & Dick Dallas
Music by Billy Taylor

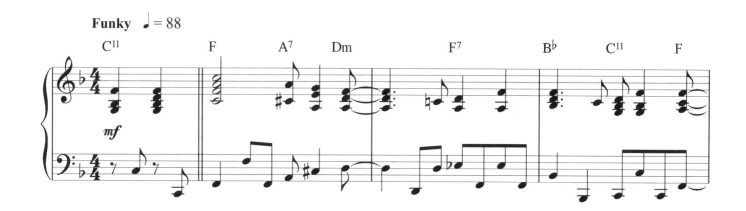

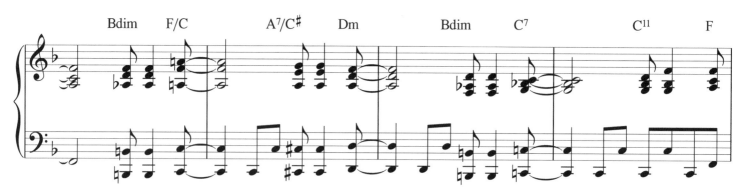

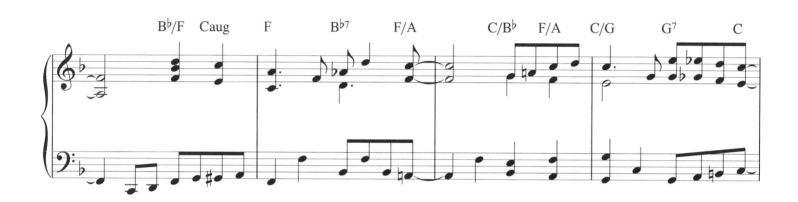

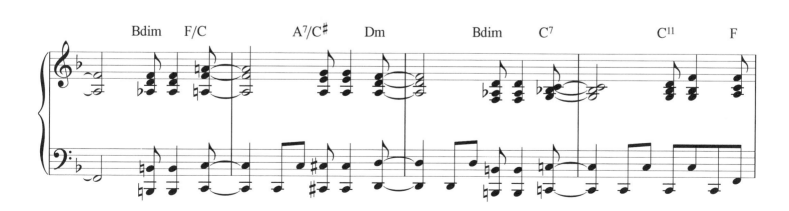

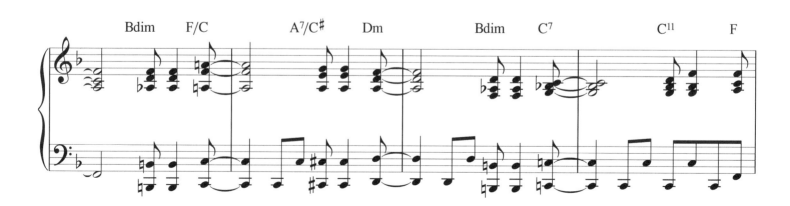

Moonlight Serenade

Words by Mitchell Parish
Music by Glenn Miller

95

My Baby Just Cares For Me

Words by Gus Kahn
Music by Walter Donaldson

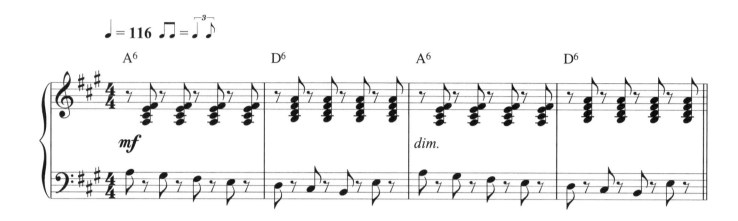

God Bless' The Child

Words & Music by Arthur Herzog Jr. & Billie Holiday

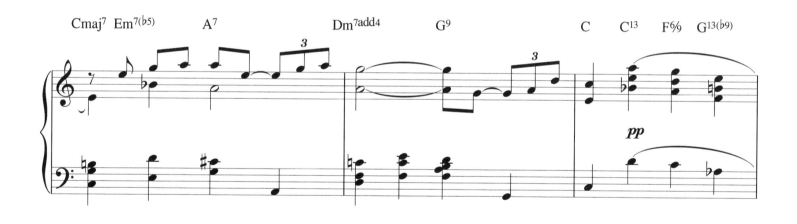

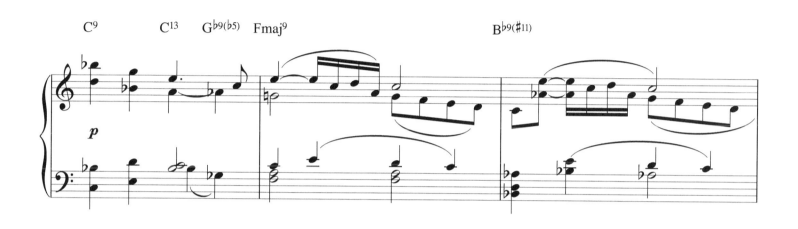

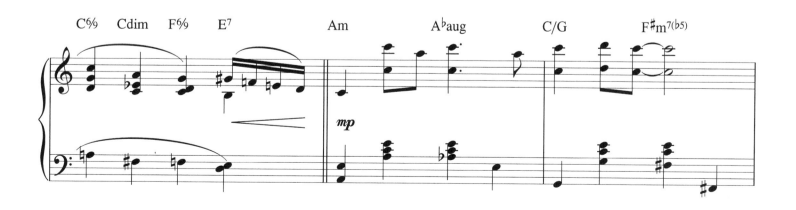

Solitude

Words by Eddie De Lange & Irving Mills
Music by Duke Ellington

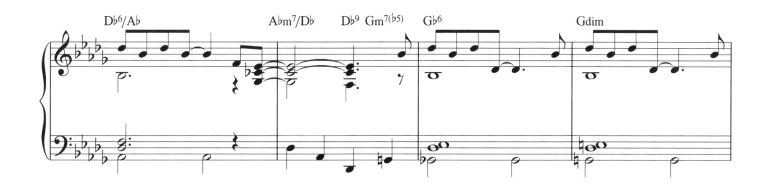

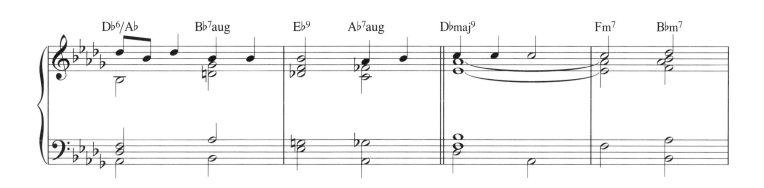

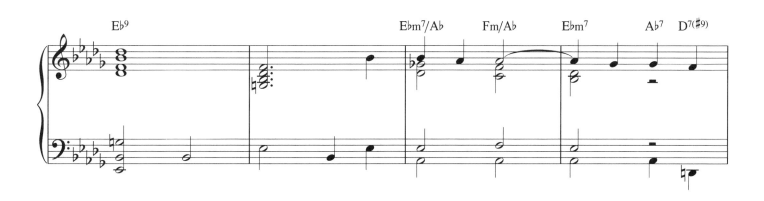

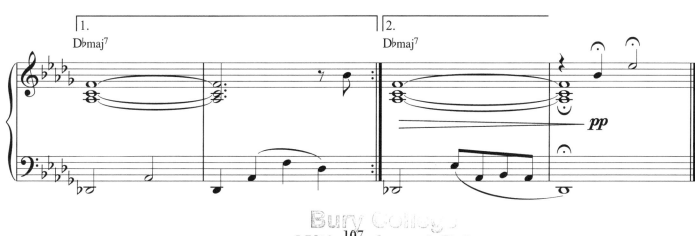

Eternity

Words & Music by Robbie Williams & Guy Chambers

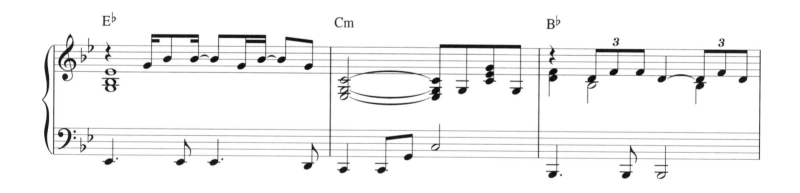

111

Fields Of Gold

Words & Music by Sting

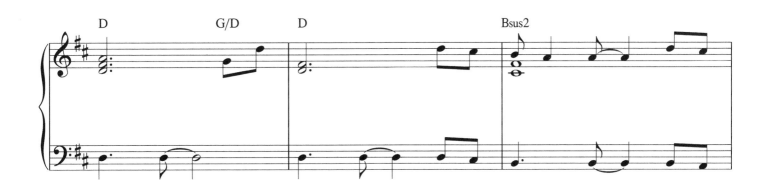

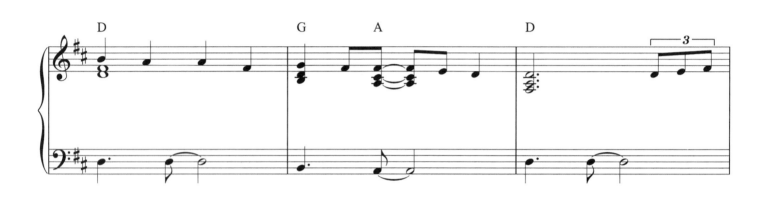

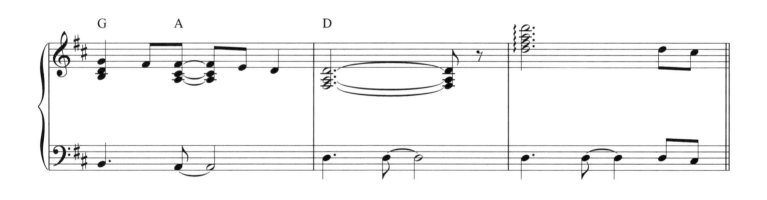

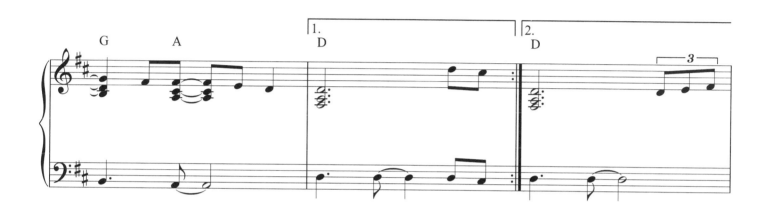

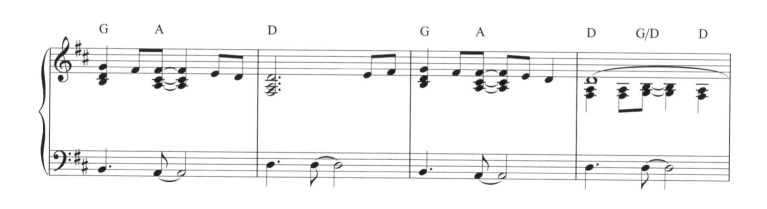

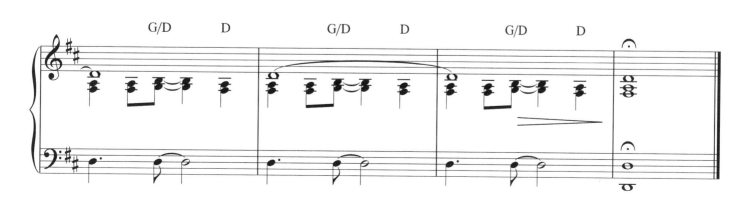

Have I Told You Lately

Words & Music by Van Morrison

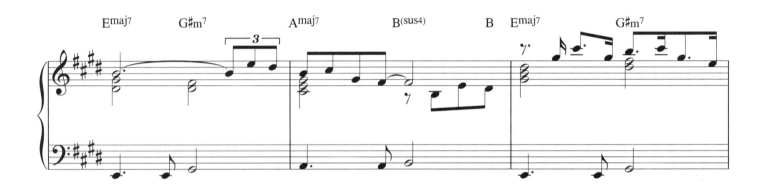

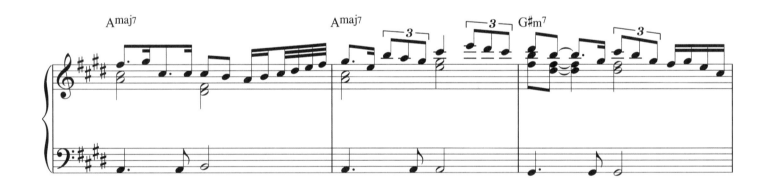

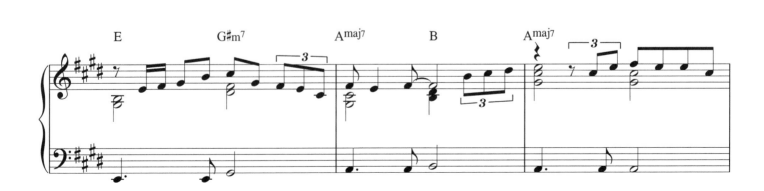

Time To Say Goodbye (Con Te Partirò)

Words by Lucio Quarantotto & Frank Peterson
Music by Francesco Sartori

121

Trouble

Words & Music by Guy Berryman, Chris Martin, Jon Buckland & Will Champion

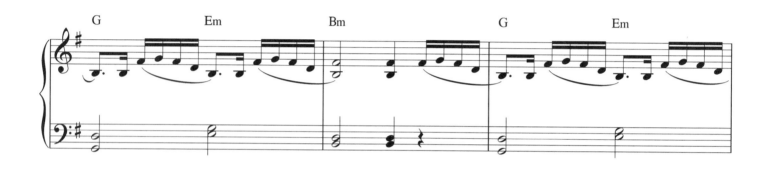

Coda

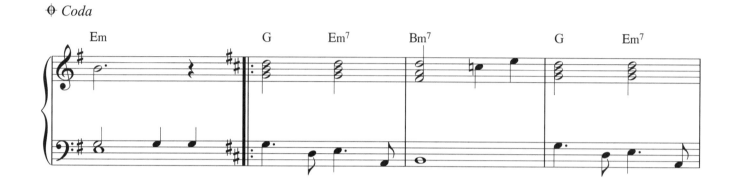

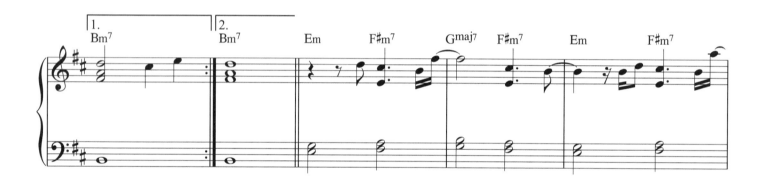

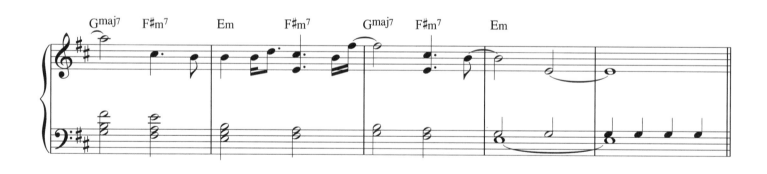

Evergreen

Words & Music by Jorgen Elofsson, Per Magnusson & David Kreuger

Your Song

Words & Music by Elton John & Bernie Taupin

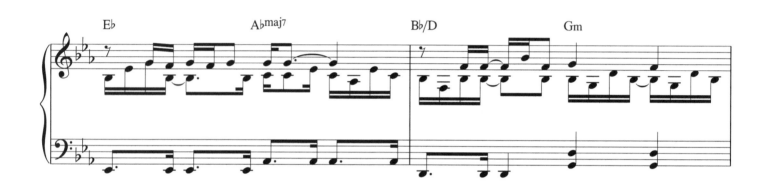

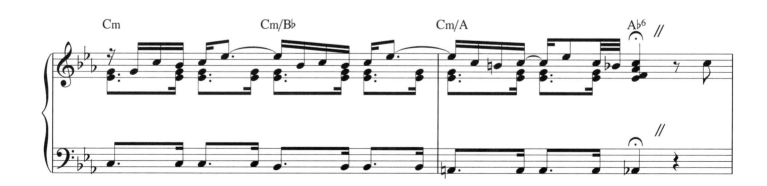

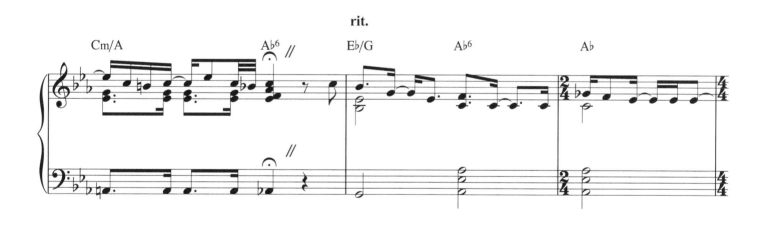

Close Every Door
(from "Joseph And The Amazing Technicolor Dreamcoat")

Words by Tim Rice
Music by Andrew Lloyd Webber

Is You Is Or Is You Ain't My Baby?

(from "Five Guys Named Moe")

Words & Music by Billy Austin & Louis Jordan

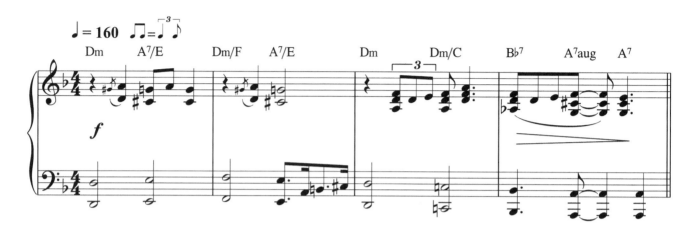

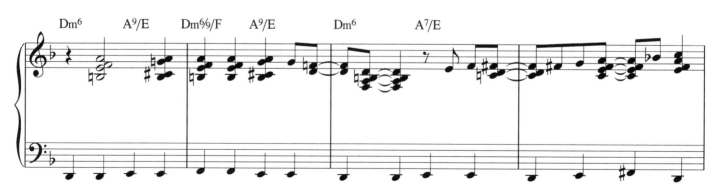

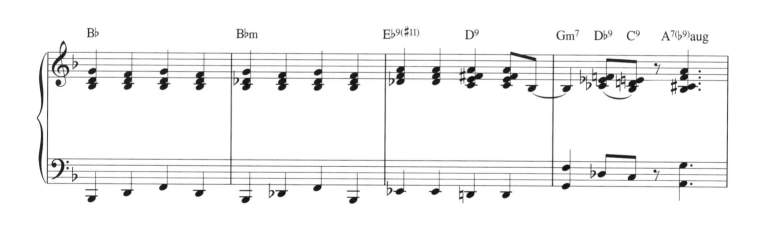

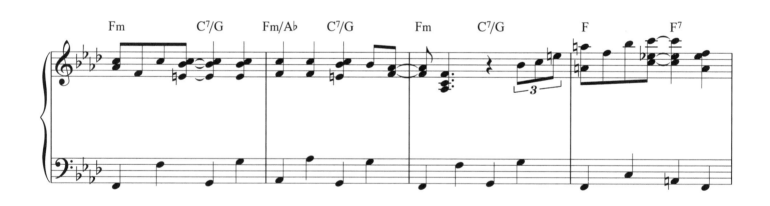

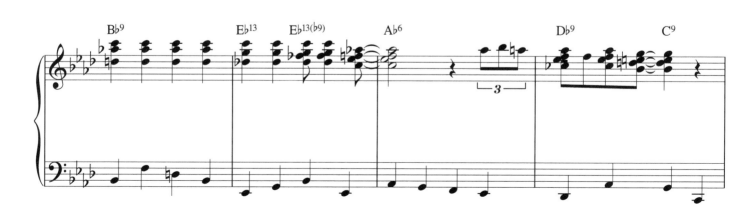

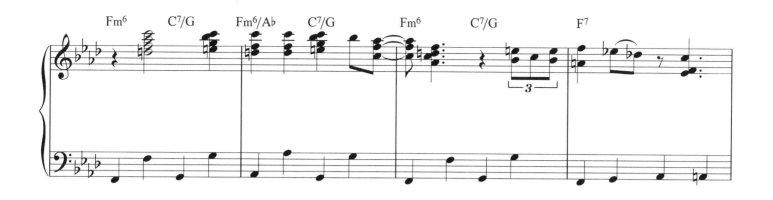

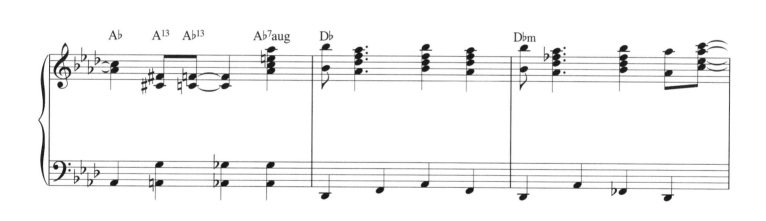

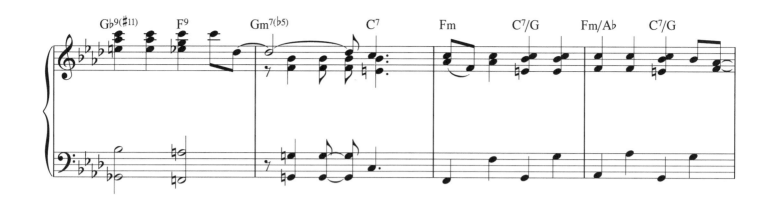

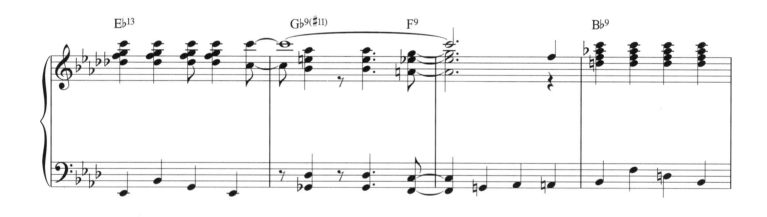

Memory
(from "Cats")

Music by Andrew Lloyd Webber
Lyrics by Trevor Nunn after T.S. Eliot

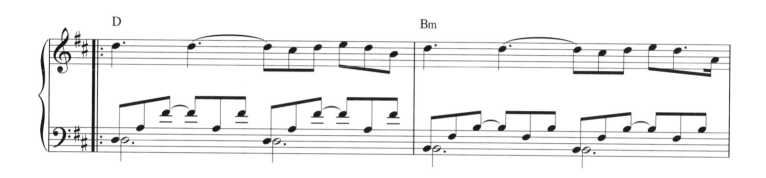

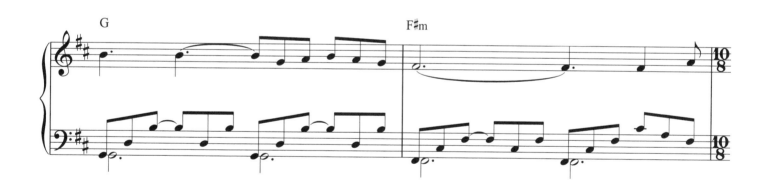

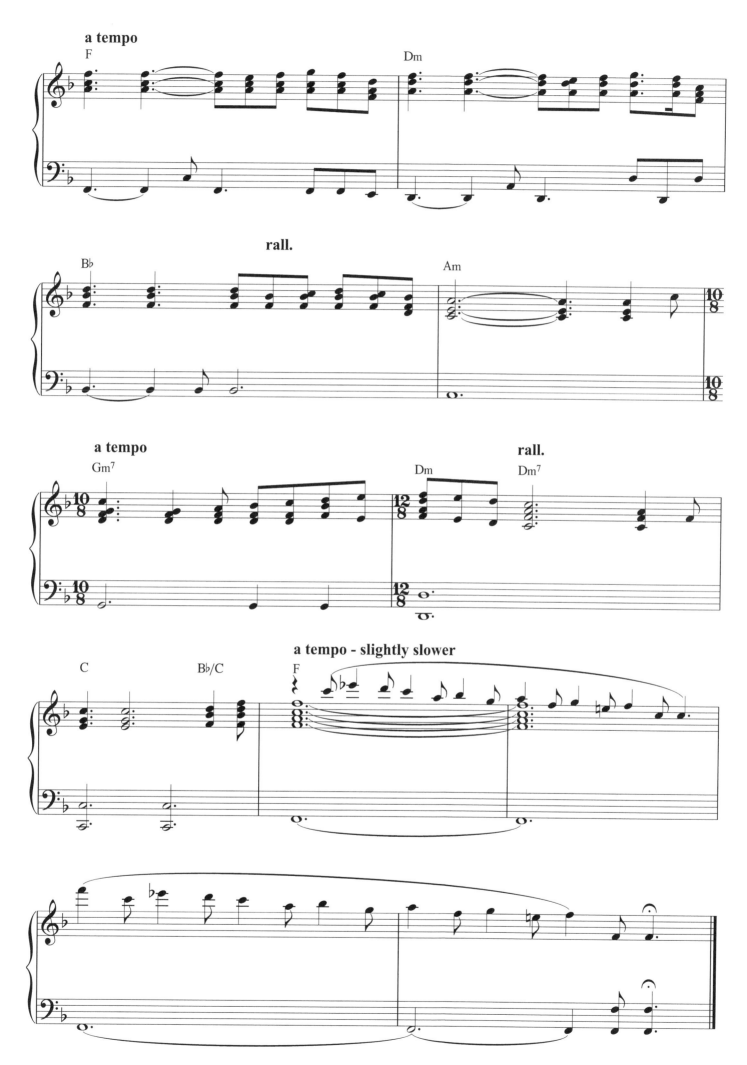

On My Own

(from "Les Misérables")

Music by Claude-Michel Schönberg
Original French Lyrics by Alain Boublil & Jean-Marc Natel
English Lyrics by Herbert Kretzmer, Trevor Nunn & John Caird

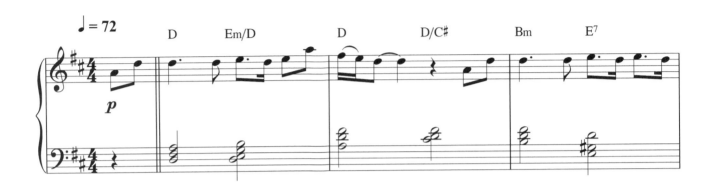

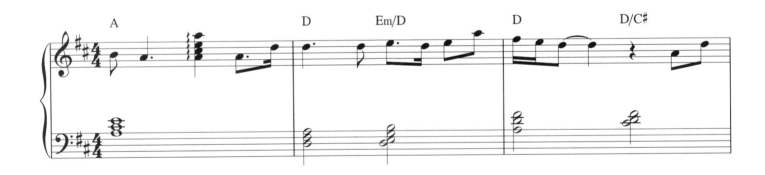

Willkommen

(from "Cabaret")

Words by Fred Ebb
Music by John Kander

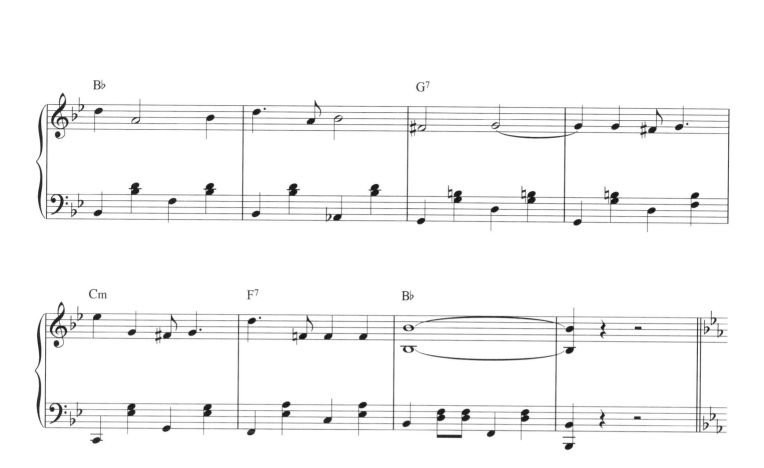

Faster

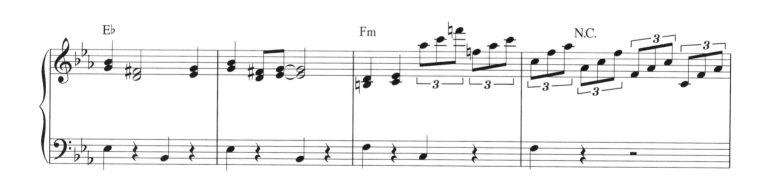

155

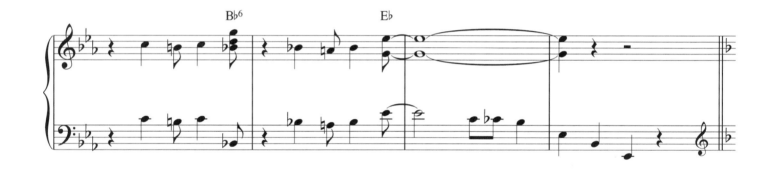

Slower

Sunrise, Sunset

(from "Fiddler On The Roof")

Words by Sheldon Harnick
Music by Jerry Bock